The Decapitation of Care

*A Short History of
the Rise and Fall of Healthcare*

DAVID HEALY

With illustrations by Billiam James

Samizdat Health

Samizdat Health Writer's Co-operative Inc.

Cover Design/Illustration: "William Petty" by Isaac Fuller (1606-1672) adapted by Billiam James.

First Printing, 2020

Title: The Decapitation of Care: A Short History of the Rise and Fall of Healthcare

ISBN: 978-1-7770565-0-6

Publisher: Samizdat Health Writer's Co-operative Inc.

www.davidhealy.org
www.samizdathealth.org

"*The quality of care is not strained.*

It droppeth as the gentle rain from heaven

Upon the place beneath. It is twice blest:

It blesseth him that gives and him that takes."

William Shakespeare, *amended*

William Petty (Without his Skull)

CONTENTS

The Rise and Fall of Healthcare

For two centuries, thanks to medical techniques, our life expectancy increased steadily, initially in Western settings and then globally. Since 2014, life expectancy in America has been falling. In 2019 it was estimated that children born now in Britain will live for three fewer years than previously expected. In many developed countries there is no longer any increase in life expectancy. Something as serious as climate change is happening.

This should come as no surprise. For three decades the greatest concentration of Fake News on the planet has centred on the medicines our doctors give us—the literature about them is ghost-written. No-one has access to the data from the clinical trials used to all but force medicines down our throats—not even regulators. And where three decades ago few of us were on 1 pill per day, now by our 40s nearly half of us are on three or more every day and medicine use is exploding in children and teenagers.

That life expectancy should fall was inevitable. As it was that the climate within what was once healthcare should also turn to winter.

The Arab Spring of 2010 got its name from the Revolutionary Spring of 1848. In response to upheavals across Europe that year Marx and Engels rushed out *The Communist Manifesto*, a pamphlet which pitched the enclosure of common lands in England leading up to 1600 as a key step in the development of "Capital". Control of land had been viewed as the source of wealth and power. Work on the land sustained most of us. But by 1848, control of manufacturing had become a competing source of wealth, and a switch to work in factories was creating a new working class.

Few of us now work on either the land or in manufacturing. As the growth of social media shows, wealth and power now lie in techniques, both physical technologies and behavioural techniques.

The power of modern techniques and their limits are most clearly visible in medicine, especially with drugs which combine physical technologies and behavioural techniques. It is here we can best see what is needed to ensure our techniques and the power that accrues to them enhance rather than diminish us and our environment.

Switching the debate about power and wealth from politics and economics to medicine brings these life and death matters closer to everyone's everyday experience. The neo-medicalism that has underpinned a transformation of healthcare into health services also sheds a light on the politics of neo-liberalism.

Our falling life expectancy and a deterioration in the climate of health services parallel changes in the wider climate and the spectacle of our oceans filling with plastic. While we are alarmed at plastic in the pristine Arctic, we have a more immediate and individual stake in the answers to being drug-wrecked or having our lives or the lives of those we love shortened. This is where the motivation to change our world rather than merely interpret it might come from.

The Origins of Medical Technique

Technologies, tools, antedate the historical record, as do the origins of behavioural technique, if only in the sense of a use of physical force to secure control. And drugs are older tools than money.

While Nature has been indifferent to our economic efforts until recently, when climates began to change, we have always faced a push-back from epidemics and plagues. Plagues held Europe in check for a millennium before measles and smallpox wiped out the American Indians, Aztecs and Incas and made Europe wealthy.

A century before the enclosure of English lands, a new technology, the printing press, triggered profound social changes. This is portrayed as putting knowledge in the hands of a greater number of people, laying the basis for what is often termed a knowledge economy—usually without any recognition of how ambiguous a term knowledge is.

In 1649, Charles I, the last absolute monarch of all English-speaking countries, was decapitated. His defeat by Cromwell stemmed in part from the labour force freed up by land enclosure moulded into a New Model Army operating with new military techniques. His decapitation opened up questions about how we govern ourselves. Thomas Hobbes, and Charles himself, in a speech from the dock, offered the view that left to ourselves life would be nasty, brutish and short and we needed governing from the top down. All governments since then through to modern technocracies agree. If we ever get Full Artificial Intelligence—Full Technique—an absolute monarchy will effectively be restored.

As Charles' head came off, new questions about how each of us govern ourselves opened up. Dr Thomas Willis in Oxford, using a novel post-mortem technique brought the brain into view in a new way, making it possible to envisage it, rather than the heart, as the governor of the body. Willis created neuroscience. In envisaging this new brain as a machine for making associations, one of his students, Dr John Locke, created psychology and put behavioural techniques on a footing that led to liberalism and now underpin social media power.

In the months after Charles' execution, Cromwell invaded Ireland, financed in part by Dr William Petty, another member of the Oxford group. In Ireland, Petty surveyed the people and the country's resources. This survey laid the basis for novel economic techniques. Petty was the first to estimate a country's Gross Domestic Product (GDP), first to propose a Free Trade agreement between two countries (Ireland and England), and first to propose that the wealth of a country might lie in its people rather than its lands.

In 1660, working with John Graunt on his Bills of Mortality for London and repeating the exercise for Dublin, Petty created a Gross Health Product. He was the first to propose judging a treatment by its outcomes rather than its theoretical basis, an early Evidence-Based Medicine.

Up to 1660, economics and medicine were branches of moral philosophy. Petty laid the basis for separate economic and medical disciplines. He referred to his work as a political medicine. His sympathies lay with government from the bottom-up.

These new economic and public health techniques led to liberalism and replaced the humoralism that had dominated medicine for two millennia by a new empirical medicine. Liberalism and medicine combined in 1789 to foment a revolution in France and the decapitation of Louis XVI by a new technique, so efficient many wondered if the guillotined head might be capable of some moments of thought and feeling—it looks like it is.

Philippe Pinel, a creator of what is now called the medical model, was in the crowd as this happened. The medical model emerged in

Dr. Philippe Pinel at the Salpêtrière in 1795, by Tony Robert-Fleury (1876).

Pinel ordering the removal of chains from patients at the Paris Asylum for insane women.

Paris in the decades on either side of 1800. The medical model linked discrete diseases to discrete malfunctions in the machinery of the body. There was no suggestion that all dis-ease would stem from diseases. Diseases were not linked to flaws of character, the moral ambiguities of an employment or the whims of Providence. The challenge to a clinician was one of pattern recognition. From what this patient tells me, or what I can see, smell or feel, is it likely there will be an underlying disorder of their biology?

Three factors led to this new model on which what we think of as modern healthcare was based until recently. It needed a sufficient collection of people in one place to allow a detection of commonalities; modern medicine needed urban settings to develop. Second, it needed a turn to linking clinical observations from living people with post-mortem findings, assisted by new technologies like stethoscopes, and a convenient disease—tuberculosis. Third was an empirical turn to judging treatments by their outcomes, pioneered by Pinel.

This medicine involved a new set of techniques and practices. A technique is more than a paradigm. It is a way of doing things within which paradigms can rise and fall. Techniques ground systems that support livelihoods. Like the guillotine or guns, they universalize, unless replaced by something apparently more efficient.

Since 1800, technique has driven medical history. Looking back, perhaps because of a bias toward seeing history as arcing toward progress, or because successful techniques often create jobs, we see a force for liberation but looking forward, we can be alarmed. The new medical techniques improved life expectancy and gave rise to what we think of as healthcare.

The same empirical approach and the availability of concentrations of people in the one place that led to a recognition of diseases, enabled a mapping of epidemics, again in Paris, and gave rise to public health medicine. In the decade before 1848, French public health doctors were a revolutionary class, whose input pinpointing occupational diseases as well as poverty and inequality as a source of ill-health lit the revolutionary fuse.

Doctors took to the barricades across Europe. One of those was Rudolf Virchow who a few months previously had been sent to Silesia by the Prussian government in Berlin to investigate a typhus epidemic and came back saying that "medicine is a social science and politics is nothing more than medicine on a grand scale".

Virchow's descriptions of the condition of the people in Silesia maps precisely onto the descriptions by Friedrich Engels, William Duncan and Charles Dickens of the conditions in which a new urban working class in England were living. These descriptions triggered *The Communist Manifesto*, which we see as a political economics tract but could see as a political medicine document.

Virchow, a liberal, and Marx and Engels offered the same remedies for the public health problem—extend the vote, enhance education, and abolish feudalism. Both saw the state withering away—government would be from the bottom-up. Marx and Engels saw workers as the revolutionary class; Virchow saw doctors in the vanguard of the revolution.

When Germany unified in 1871, its first chancellor, Bismarck, aware of the revolutionary drive within medicine, was interested to block any alliance between medicine and socialism. Aware that insurance had stabilized new ventures such as risky trade routes, tourism, and hazardous industrial jobs, Bismarck figured on stabilizing the new German nation-state with health insurance—the first-ever national health scheme. His move co-opted medicine for the state as doctors needed to register with the system in order to participate. Medicine was on its way to becoming part of an establishment.

While Bismarck was putting health insurance in place, using a new technique based on synthetic dyes, a group of physicians linked to Robert Koch created bacteriology. These dyes also created modern pharmacology. The new bacteriology and pharmacology combined in the image of a Magic Bullet.

Bacteriology, by which they meant pharmacology, was later portrayed by 20th-century critics of biomedicine as doing little to reduce mortality from tuberculosis compared with social measures. The most significant and successful municipal mobilisation against tuberculosis was instituted by Hermann Biggs in New York in the 1890s, but Biggs' dramatic success hinged on his acceptance of what bacteriology had to say about the causes and nature of tuberculosis.

The triumph of bacteriology and clinical medicine around this time is sometimes portrayed as a plot by a medical mafia supported by powerful foundations or government. Bacteriology certainly helped the medical model take hold but probably mainly because the new science brought new jobs for plumbers, painters, brewers, the chemical industry (disinfectants) and advertising industry (adverts for new toilets, disinfectants and food hygiene aids) in its wake. A lot of non-medical people had an incentive to make Pasteur and Koch household names. The force of history that sweeps certain views aside often stems from the job opportunities that open up on the "victorious" side. (The victorious side need not be the correct side as the cholesterol story indicates).

Meanwhile a more powerful force than bacteriology had taken a primary lead in shaping medicine.

Military Medicine

American medicine in the 19th century is portrayed as behind the curve with American physicians having to visit Paris and Berlin as part of their medical education.

In the 1840s, however, anaesthesia was developed in Boston. This technique raised a question—did the ends, a better surgical outcome, justify a means that risked killing someone? We collectively decided it did.

This answer laid the basis for a flowering of surgical techniques in the American Civil War. The North's successful campaign involved efficient medical provisioning. Jonathan Letterman organized First Aid stations on the battlefield, developed an ambulance service and the initial Red Cross conventions, instituted triage at field hospitals, and set up a grid of hospitals behind the front lines, with both triage and hospitals oriented in a novel fashion to ensure hygienic conditions. New firearm technologies led to new injuries and new surgical operations, as well as a use of plaster of Paris, and better analgesia through a new technique—the hypodermic syringe. Short of supplies, Julian Chisholm, on the Confederate side, created a new inhalational technique that reduced the amount of chloroform needed by 90%.

Despite these developments, as with every war up till then, more soldiers died from medical conditions than from enemy action. War has been an experiment with a grisly outcome, success being measured in terms of numbers dying from military as compared with medical causes. The first successful war, in the sense of fewer troops dying from medical rather than martial causes, was fought by the Japanese against the Russians in 1904, with the Japanese adopting methods from the American Civil War.

The Civil War led to an awareness of the need for a placement of urban hospitals in grid systems that facilitate access to treatment in the

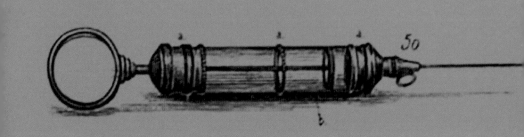

case of accidents, a need for Casualty, later Emergency Departments, a need for civilian training in First Aid and urban ambulance services. War, rather than bio or social, private or public medicine, created the provisioning of medical services in urban settings that is a major component of health services today.

The Great War put orthopaedic surgery, rehabilitation medicine, prostheses, plastic (later cosmetic) surgery, mobile X-ray units, and blood transfusions on the map. The role of the military, especially the American military, in medical, especially surgical, developments continues to this day with the military initiating robotic and telesurgery programs and having an increasing input to vaccination programs.

The Great War arguably made Freud and trauma. Before the war, a trauma was a physical wound. Freud's brand of psychodynamics was one among many. The conditions variously termed shellshock then, and PTSD now, were more effectively treated by other behavioural techniques than Freud's but his was the brand that emerged from the War.

This may have been because Freud's nephew Edward Bernays helped create the public relations industry in America after the War. Americans were also quick to realise the value of embodying messages in the new cinematic medium opening up in Hollywood, laying the basis for a propaganda industry, closely linked to military needs ever since, and to behavioural economics (nudging) now.

Before the Great War, within healthcare women had been seen primarily as nurses. By 1918, women ran many European hospitals and undertook the surgery on the home front, while men became hysterical on the battlefront, something not previously thought possible. Our views of gender roles changed radically.

War fostered the development of preventive medicine created by Sara Josephine Baker in New York. In 1908, Baker demonstrated that focusing on mothers and infants before and after birth, ensuring hygiene and adequate nutrition, dramatically reduced infant mortality rates. This led to women and children's services aimed at strengthening individual resilience. Baker forced most countries to become as pronatalist as the Catholic Church, when she noted that more soldiers were dying in cribs than on Europe's battlefields.

When Charles I was decapitated, Providence was still seen as the main driver of history. For 250 years after that individual genius (great men) was seen as the driver. By the time the Great War was over there was a compelling case that techniques, or the power that accrues to those who hold the most effective techniques, drives history forward.

Techniques come with risks. There are the inherent risks of anesthesia, drugs, guns and smart phones. From cosmetic surgery to tests for blood lipids, technologies drive consumption—even without additional techniques designed to persuade us to consume "because we are worth it". Techniques put us in the firing line; they work and so if something goes wrong, somebody has messed up. There has been an accident with guns or drugs that is our fault, when in fact what has happened was inevitable rather than accidental.

Just before the Great War, the American Medical Association (AMA) supported universal health insurance. By the end of the War, AMA opposed universal health insurance, in part because by 1920, America had more hospitals than the rest of the world combined. These hospitals did surgery—not medicine—and today Americans have more medical devices in their bodies than the rest of the world combined.

In the 1930s, America's hospitals created private health insurance to help them ride out the Depression. The absence of universal health coverage in America is therefore to some extent a consequence of the Civil War.

Another consequence was the opioid epidemic in the years surrounding 1900. This was facilitated by use of morphine delivered through hypodermic syringes in the Civil War. This epidemic led to a new medical policing technique—the idea of prescription-only status for some medicines.

Meanwhile, the new bacteriologically-driven craze for cleanliness in the 1880s which replaced wallpaper with paint laced with lead, began to show up in mental disabilities in children and perhaps to the epidemic of schizophrenia in the 19th and 20th centuries. The new cleanliness probably contributed to polio epidemics, with the first major outburst occurring in New York in 1916.

Centrally-Planned Medicine

There is nothing about health or medicine in the work of Max Weber, although, like Marx, Weber was afflicted with ill-health throughout his life and died prematurely. In a famous 1919 lecture, he described political leaders as individuals who, like doctors, had to embrace the necessity of doing evil in order to achieve a good that might consist in getting a nation to take its medicine. He also drew attention to a growing bureaucracy operating behind the politicians, and a turn to bureaucratic technique as a form of government that risked imprisoning us all in an Iron Cage.

In the 1920s preventive medicine emerged and fed into a new set of public health bureaucracies. These saw the nation as a garden in which medical planners could foster the growth of healthy plants and remove weeds that might contaminate the national stock. This had a notable expression in a eugenic movement that led to sterilizations and a focus on mothers as a potential weak link in the maintenance of the national stock.

The clearest expression came in German-speaking countries between 1937 and 1943, when a great number of mentally handicapped individuals, among whom were many children, along with mentally ill patients were eliminated. This process, aimed at strengthening the *Volk*, preceded the elimination of aliens, also regarded as vitiating the *Volk*. This was a centrally planned top-down social initiative.

As these initiatives took shape, German pharmaceutical companies produced the first Magic Bullet, a sulpha drug with antibiotic properties, Prontosil. This was followed by penicillin, streptomycin, tetracycline and other antibiotics. The sulpha drugs also gave rise to diuretics, antihypertensives and hypoglycemic agents. Psychotropic drugs, steroid and other hormones, oral contraceptives, and chemotherapies followed. Public collaboration helped fund and find a vaccine for polio, opening up prospects for yet further vaccinations.

These new pharmaceutical commodities dramatically changed the pharmaceutical industry. American companies vertically integrated— producing their own compounds, marketing them and reaping the profits. This industry, which until 1950 had been an industrial minnow, within a decade became the most profitable in America, and was on its way to having the most effective marketing apparatus of any industry.

As this happened, a basic research program funded by the American government, operating through the National Institutes of Health (NIH), laid the basis for much of the developments in what is now called biomedicine, especially in neuroscience. With infections now manageable, the focus turned to non-communicable diseases—heart attacks, strokes and cancer. The identification of risk factors such as obesity and smoking along with the first heart transplants in the mid-1960s made the conquest of these diseases also seem inevitable.

In the 1950s, this flourishing of the biomedical sciences was linked to a striking openness. Books appeared on the side effects of the new miracle drugs, on occupational medicine and on the impact of pesticides and other breakthroughs on the environment.

As the War was ending, Friedrich Hayek's *The Road to Serfdom* also appeared warning that the virus of central planning was inimical to human freedom, culture and science; that there was an urgent need to return to a 19th century liberalism that had found its clearest expression in Britain and America, although neither of these countries had entirely escaped the virus of central planning in Hayek's view. There is nothing in Hayek about health, despite the striking role of central planning in medicine.

Few thought it was possible to return to the 19th century freedoms. Modern economies—and modern medicine—had become too complex. Despite Germany's defeat, its example and the American experience of WW II, which was intensely planned and involved a command economy, suggested that managed economies were the way of the future. Americans returning from the War signed on for degrees in a new science—management (MBAs).

As this was happening, sponsored by socially rather than biomedically oriented American foundations, cybernetics took shape. This was the science of computing and the information flows it gave rise to. Its leading figure, Norbert Wiener, pointed to the feedback loops in everything from thermostats to computing and homeostasis. Feedback loops like this are one-dimensional but aggregating feedback loops can create the appearances of an organizational map, that with appropriate reviews of performance and benchmarking against standards, was adopted and relabelled Systems Theory. This became the basis for the new management science, which put a premium on operational thinking. Its advocates claimed cybernetics explained why free markets work.

In 1964, just before he died, Wiener warned that operational thinking could apply to lower-order closed systems but not to higher-order human activities which are open systems in which choice and responsibility are critical. When we engage with closed systems, we hand over responsibility and must remember this. He foresaw a real peril in the development of what we now call Full Artificial Intelligence but could also call Full Technique.

Social tension was building in the post-war years. On the one side there was a rising affluence, that appealed to many, as caught by J.K. Galbraith in his 1958 book *The Affluent Society*. On the other side was a new concern about conformity and management caught in books like *The Organisation Man* and Galbraith's *The New Industrial State*, which argued that rather than satisfying our needs, corporations were creating wants for the goods they could supply. As awareness grew of Eastern European totalitarianism there was talk of a more subtle and even more effective totalitarianism in the West—mediated through bureaucrats, now called managers.

These tensions mapped on to clashing perceptions of biomedical developments. Many saw the cornucopia of new drugs and medical advances up to and including heart transplants as a crossing of new frontiers as steadily as the space program was. Others viewed the new capabilities as offering a potential for behavioural control. Michel Foucault and later Ivan Illich described a medicalisation that was enslaving rather than liberating us and a medical gaze that was dehumanising.

Herbert Marcuse in *One-Dimensional Man* charted our turn away from philosophy and toward operational or instrumental thinking. A turn to doing rather than thinking. He noted a turn to numbers that in the "culture industries" meant if more people went to Disney movies than Shakespeare plays, Hollywood would do Disney and not Shakespeare.

Within medicine the times also saw a turn to numbers—for blood pressure, blood sugar and cholesterol as well as numbers linked to behavioural rating scales. Where before, it had seemed clinically important to distinguish between malignant and benign hypertensions or between proper melancholia and a reactive distress, the availability of treatments that might drive the figures in a preferred direction put a premium on doing rather than exploring.

In the 1930s, George Rosen, like many Jews unable to get into medicine in New York, enrolled in Berlin instead, where he became aware of Rudolph Virchow and his claim that politics is nothing more than medicine on a grand scale. In a 1958 history of public health, Rosen transformed Virchow into a patron saint of social medicine, helping to set up a divide between biomedicine and social medicine. In fact, Virchow had put the cell on the map as the fundamental site of disease, the key biomedical belief, and he had opposed most "social" developments in medicine—including health insurance. Rosen's divide of medicine into bad bio and good social siblings introduced a fatal weakness that helped conceal the role of power and technique, whether bio or social, in shaping medicine.

The clashing medical currents became most turbulent in psychiatry. In the 1960s, LSD appeared to call the entire social order into question, the oral contraceptives dramatically changed relations between the sexes, while the minor tranquilizers disinhibited. But in 1968, students revolting in Paris ransacked the offices of Jean Delay, the discoverer of the first antipsychotic and all but the creator of modern psychiatry, for his role in creating chemical straitjackets. Antipsychiatrists declared psychoses a political rather than a medical event.

While tanks rolled into Prague in 1968 and crushed the Prague Spring, the response in the West to the medical and political turbulence was a turn to operational or cybernetic thinking.

Where there had been a growing use of economic metrics like Petty's GDP from the 1930s, after a coup in Chile in the mid-1970s the supply of money was given a thermostat-like function in the economy. The supply of money would be held constant whatever the consequences for the Chilean people. This monetarism was justified on the basis that whether you were a capitalist or a socialist, money supposedly didn't smell.

The turn to operational, or thermostat, thinking in medicine shows in the adoption in 1976 of operational criteria as a basis for a new *Diagnostic and Statistical Manual* for mental disorders. Just as with a policy of following the money supply regardless of the state of a people, it was decided that a disorder could be designated as depression if, for instance, someone met 5 of 9 criteria, regardless of the worldviews of biomedical or socially-oriented researchers. It's now clear, this maneuver came at a cost of labelling someone as depressed who might meet criteria because they were pregnant or influenzal or might decide themselves they met criteria for all kinds of disorders. Operational criteria don't smell. They formed the basis for a neo-medicalism.

Reshaping Pharmaceutical Technique

The signal event shaping medicine in the late 20th century and ever since was the marketing in 1956 of a French drug, thalidomide, as a sleeping pill by a German company. This caused horrific birth defects, then an unimaginable drug wreck. The shock triggered an international crisis that led to an amendment to the US Food and Drugs Act in 1962. The essential feature of this Act was a turn to a recently invented and poorly understood technique, Randomized Controlled Trials (RCTs) to establish the efficacy of new drugs. This was copied by other regulators worldwide. Prior to this, the regulatory focus had been on the safety of drugs.

The first RCT took place in 1947 and focused on the use of streptomycin for tuberculosis patients. It showed an RCT could work in

principle but it missed many of the effects of standard clinical trials detected. There were a small number of advocates for RCTs, among whom was Louis Lasagna, but no great rush to switch from standard trials to RCTs. In 1956, Lasagna suggested that RCTs might underpin the addition of an efficacy criterion to the profile of effects of a drug prior to regulatory approval. The thalidomide crisis gave him an opportunity to include this idea in the 1962 FDA Act.

At the time, there was no sense that the focus on a primary efficacy outcome that RCTs require might make them a gold-standard way to hide adverse events. Even though RCTs were being made the gateway to getting drugs on the market, there was no sense that their use might be taken over by industry and trial data might end up sequestered. It was thought that if one RCT showed a drug to be effective, all other trials would do the same and so a regulatory criterion was set at two positive trials. It was not yet clear that while two trials might be positive, a greater number could be negative. Nor that a demonstration of benefits on surrogate outcomes could lead to the approval of a drug that killed more people than it saved.

There was no sense of just how heterogenous clinical populations are and how this might lead treatment effects, good or bad, to disappear into the background noise, and how companies might be able to use this. There was no sense that where a disorder and a drug produce superficially similar clinical features, as with the heart failure in diabetes or on anti-diabetic drugs, RCTs would be unable to disentangle the two and companies could also use this.

RCTs in fact are clinically useless. When RCTs of a fertilizer tell a farmer this fertilizer works, s/he can assume it will work in all other fields, but this is not true of a medicine. RCTs tell a doctor nothing about which drug will work for the patient in front of them.

The drugs that have come on the market since 1962 have mostly been less effective than those that came into use before 1962. Almost none save lives. Surgery, in contrast, which with its clean surgical strikes is much more suited to an RCT than anything but Magic Bullets that affect every body system, has moved forward much more clearly—without input from RCTs.

But this regulatory requirement for RCTs let bureaucrats and others claim that regulation was now based on science and that not only were medicines better as a result but that the practice of medicine was more rational. In the 1980s, with an accumulation of RCTs, this viewpoint led to Guidelines—based largely on industry trials. In 1990, this viewpoint underpinned a push to Evidence-Based Medicine.

Even if done by angels, RCTs are a technique, and like all techniques are one-dimensional and not readily able to cope with internal contradictions, especially the contradiction that involves trying to bring good out of the use of a poison. The results we get using RCTs depend on the intentions put into their deployment. If they are regarded as value-neutral and as delivering valid results regardless of the intentions of those who run them, they are likely to diminish rather than enhance human health. Very few RCTs are done by angels.

From Healthcare to Health Services

In 1970, the word risk featured in the titles or abstracts of 200 academic articles. By 1990 it was 20,000. We didn't have risks until recently. Risk is driven by numbers.

Risk came into play in politics and medicine in the 1980s. Risk Societies crystallized on the political radar with a 1992 book by Ulrich Beck, which argued that we rather than Nature now posed the greatest risks to ourselves and to Nature. Managing risks was adopted by a centre ground keen to promote a Third Way between the "old-style" politics of left and right.

Risk appeared in medicine in 1981, when Geoffrey Rose, a London physician, claimed that the traditional medical focus on disease was wrong. Infant and maternal healthcare had succeeded, he argued, by focusing on children and mothers when well to prevent them getting ill. Just as getting everyone to wear a seat belt can save more lives than getting joy-riders alone to wear seat belts, so focusing on a population, most of whom are at minimal risk, would save more lives than focusing on high risk or diseased individuals. To eliminate heart attacks, medicine must treat all elevations of blood pressure, cholesterol and sugar.

The idea of treating entire populations fascinated public health departments, even though medicating people who are well is crucially different to preventing them from smoking, using salt or wearing seatbelts. No-one seemed worried at the prospect of "poisoning" hundreds of people to prevent a cardiac death, even after clinical trials demonstrated increased mortality.

Risk Prevention later badged as Health Promotion invited us to manage risks lying within us rather than in our environment. Doctors didn't argue. While there was some promotion of healthy lifestyles, preventing risks meant dishing out more medicines, not less. Governments and insurers saw the promised cost savings as justifying mandatory screening and withholding information about the harms of treatment in case anyone might be put-off. As with vaccines, the population risks seemingly lay in non-treatment.

There was a switch from the traditional medical focus on treating acute life-threatening crises such as infections and traumatic injuries, with a later emphasis on heart attacks, strokes and cancer to what is called Chronic Disease Management—even though almost none of those being managed have anything medically wrong with them. They have mild thinning of their bones, a wheeze, minimal elevations of blood pressure, blood sugars, or lipids.

Just a few years before, in 1976, the pharmaceutical industry had told the US Congress their share prices were about to collapse. The branded industry was facing competition from generic drugs. The other way to maintain share price is to "grow" the market. With the development of antihypertensives, hypoglycemics, and new drugs for osteoporosis and lipid lowering, risk prevention could be used to give everyone several "diseases" at the same time and in perpetuity.

In 1984 the US drugs market was worth just over $20 billion. In 1989, GSK's Zantac, an antacid, became the first blockbuster drug—a drug to gross $1 billion per annum. A decade later Pfizer's Lipitor was grossing $13 billion per annum. By 2000, more money was being spent in the United States on marketing the risks of cholesterol than on the country's research on dementia, autism, arthritis, multiple sclerosis, sickle cell anemia and other traditional medical disorders combined. Company share prices held up.

Where patients were once typically on one medicine only, seven is now the norm for anyone over 50. Anyone put on an antibiotic is likely to already be on some combination of antihypertensives, statins, bisphosphonates, hypoglycemics and psychotropics. Medical wisdom, traditionally skeptical of vitamins, dietary fads and other fashions whipped up on the basis of notional risks, had a Damascene conversion to Risk Management.

This conversion helped transform healthcare into health services. From the 1950s, employment in developed economies began to transition from manufacturing to a new service sector, as it had from agriculture to manufacturing a century earlier. This sector encompassed catering, hospitality, banking, insurance and a growing number of other services and was where the new management took root.

Health was not part of this new sector because the outcomes for treating heart attacks, strokes, cancer and madness were too uncertain and it was not possible to bring products to people as required in the service sector.

But treating elevations of blood pressure or bone thinning in contrast produced quality outcomes, in the sense of the same outcome every time. This permitted a switch to marketing services to consumers. Health was folded into the service sector, with new managers who might have rotated in from Big Tobacco or Fast Food.

The creation of guidelines assisted this transition. Before that managers had to depend on clinical discretion as regards the treatment of individual patients and the configuration of services in general. Now guidelines established standards of care that managers, whether in the private or public sectors, could insist their employees met. Clinical and patient discretion now became a risk to be managed by an "industry".

The pharmaceutical companies meanwhile took to providing free peak-flow meters to doctors, confident that these would increase diagnoses of asthma and the prescription of anti-asthmatic medicines. They provided free bone scanners confident that hints of bone-thinning would lead to prescriptions of their new bisphosphonate drugs. Standard blood test forms include glucose and lipid levels, and so we all got screened for these without our consent. Many health plans quickly required doctors to undertake such screening of their clientele (us), and to offer treatments to those in risk categories.

Despite the huge increase in company income, companies could still claim their treatments remained at an unchanged 10% fraction of health budgets. This happened because risk prevention strategies called for screening programs, followed by auditors and managers when the expected benefits failed to materialise, and this grew the non-drug budget to a greater extent than the drugs budget, making health services increasingly uneconomic.

In the 1870s, weighing scales antedated by a few years the first reports of anorexia nervosa. Eating disorders increased and later spread globally in parallel with the spread of weighing scales from pharmacies to our homes and then from the West to worldwide. In the same way, measurements have become the illnesses and neuroses that our treatments now treat and the mushrooming of Health Apps will create new pandemics.

The profusion of measurement technologies and the turn to a service industry, both psychotherapeutic and pharmacologic, that brings

dis-ease to us is a recipe for an epidemic of identity disorders. This appears to be what we now face. In addition to measurement disorders, there is pressure from enhancement options linked to cosmetic pills or cosmetic surgery. A growing number of us have been taking up neurodiverse, gender-fluid, and other dis-ease options, and have a general sense of having been traumatized. This pressure that focuses on us "because we are worth it" fractures communities.

Risk-Benefit

In the 1960s and 1970s, the automobile and chemical industries used cost-benefit analyses to nullify the push to regulate automobiles, lead in paint, chemicals in the environment and other hazards. The cost of seat belts in terms of jobs lost was easily "established" but it was supposedly impossible to work out the savings from their benefits.

From 1980 onwards risk-benefit analyses of drugs turn cost-benefit analyses inside out. Industry conjured health economics out of thin air to demonstrate how much treatment benefits would save the economy, where estimating the benefits from seat belts or airbags had been impossible.

The onus was left to patients or doctors to cost any risks of treatment. By 1990, the mantra that RCTs deliver the only reliable information on medicines had taken hold. With cost-benefit analyses in other industries, industry won because the studies showing lives lost were drowned out by industry studies. In medicine, industry ran all the studies.

As regards RCT benefits, these are changes on rating scales or cholesterol levels rather than lives saved or people restored to work. There are few new drugs apart from Triple Therapy for AIDS for which we can make a valid risk-benefit analysis. Aside from industry's favoured harm of not getting treatment, RCTs are not designed to detect harms. Where harms happen, ghostwriters now make them vanish. By 1990, industry realized regulators could do nothing in the face of their claims that the risk-benefit analysis for their drug remained favourable. And so until a Merck removed a Vioxx from the market, drugs were safe, even if they caused heart attacks, diabetes, suicide, gambling or promiscuity.

Risk-benefit analyses based on clinical trial data were a juggernaut that flattened regulators and the media and will do so until such time as life expectancies begin to fall and someone gets to grips with why.

In this looking-glass world, FDA's 1962 effectiveness mandate is gold. The precautionary principle works for pharma because the way to reduce risk is to treat. In a dangerous world, better to nuke than to balance risks. In other industries regulators aim at safety. No one in the Securities Exchange Commission, or airline regulation advises on efficacy. The concern is to make investing and travel safe. Road safety makes sense; road efficacy doesn't. The effectiveness criterion, however, makes junk medicines more valuable to industry than life-saving treatments.

In this Alice in Wonderland market, patients injured by a drug or doctors concerned about marketing, find other patients and doctors view them as an enemy of the people. Patients on antidepressants hear the message "it may be wiser not to treat" morph into "your illness is trivial". Doctors giving a statin hear their good intentions questioned. Both mobilize without prompting from Pharma. RCTs provide the information that transform chemicals into medicines. If RCTs deny the risks, the only rational course of action for patients and doctors is to defend the drug and brand attacks as anti-medical and irrational.

But if we adhere to the guidelines for managing all risks, we exponentially increase the risk of killing or maiming people, as five medicines or more per day reduces life expectancy and increases hospitalization rates. We now all live in a Medical Sheffield where we get diseases and die prematurely because the poisoning from our medicines blots out the sun and contaminates the air. The question is how long will it take for the evidence of falling life expectancies to trigger a clean-up?

Whether the focus is on prostate risks based on a deeply flawed test, counteracting the effect of poor diets or sedentary living, the New Medical State is not about treating diseases. It's about identities and the management of risks to our identity bundled up in branded disorders that encompass ever more of our lives.

On a management level, it's about meeting targets. And in the effort to meet targets, trust is lost. If I break my leg badly enough to need a metal plate, I let a surgeon "mutilate" me, confident that this is what she would choose to do in a similar situation, things can go wrong, but it's a risk we choose to and take trust likely grows from the outcome. On the other hand, if I feel fine but get talked into taking an osteoporosis drug by a doctor who would never take these drugs herself—because their potential to produce a spiral fracture of the femur—then trust is corroded and healing compromised.

The Berlin Wall

In the 1980s two events cut across these medical and political developments. An old-style medical illness, AIDS, turned up like Banquo's ghost at the celebration of the new Risk Prevention (McMedicine) reign. AIDS activists railed against the Iron Cage of bureaucratic procedure and indifference that blocked their access to life-saving drugs—such as thalidomide and AZT that may have killed as many patients as were killed by the virus. They steered a path between the left and right of politics with an insistence on their right to live the lives they chose to live.

℞

BLOOD SUGAR
PILLS

DIABETES DRUG AVANDIA
REDUCES BLOOD SUGAR AND
LIFE EXPECTANCY. LINKED
TO 83,000 HEART ATTACK DEATHS
AVANDIA (ROSIG... ...AXOSMITHKLINE
...ECULIN (TRO... ...RKE-...
...NUVIA... ...ONGLYZA...
...S AGE... ...ERS B BYETTA
...TOZA... AGLUTIDE)

As AIDs activism took shape, a dissident movement mobilized in Eastern Europe against a bureaucratic dictatorship that unlike traditional dictatorships claimed to rule in the name of the majority, claimed legitimacy before the law and looked permanent. Czech and Polish dissidents did not see the West as free. Their goal was to give people the right to live the lives they chose to live. But when their efforts brought the Berlin Wall down in 1989, their success was cast as a triumph of neo-liberalism and an end of history.

The fall of the Wall was followed by the discovery of Triple Therapy for AIDs, a discovery made without an RCT. This was also hailed as evidence that the Western way of doing things was the only way. In fact, Triple Therapy has been one of the few therapies since the 1960s that saves lives and the pharmaceutical industry has since then clearly taken a position that saving lives is bad for business.

The Access to Medicines campaign that arose from efforts to bring Triple Therapy to a global set of patients was one of medicine's greatest moral and political triumphs but continuing campaigns for access to high-cost drugs now channel patients toward polypharmacy and an earlier death. How did this happen?

Assembly Lines

In the 1950s and early 1960s drug discovery was serendipitous, with the new drugs driving developments in biology rather than stemming from them.

Advised by a new breed of management consultants in the 1960s, the pharmaceutical industry switched from management by chemists and physicians to management by managers. They restructured, and outsourced clinical trials to Contract Research Organizations (CRO), now a $30 billion business.

They outsourced medical writing to medical writing agencies, staffed by PhD's whose brief it was to turn around product that included review articles, reports of clinical trials, opinion pieces and expert briefs for drug submissions to a faster and more predictable timetable than academics.

Drug development was outsourced following the Bayh-Dole Act in 1980. Around 1980, industry initiatives aimed at rational drug development using high-speed throughput in assays aimed at profiling the receptors drugs bound to. This program failed and its failure accelerated the turn to outsourcing.

Around 2000, public relations (propaganda) was outsourced. If anything about drug hazards or drug costs turn up in the public domain now, it is rare to spot anyone speaking for the industry. Independent academics are mobilized instead.

Within industry, there has been a proliferation of protocols for good laboratory, good clinical trials, and good public relations practices, so that those working in companies see their industry as more ethical than it was in the 1950s and more adherent to good practices than medical academics are now. That said, the PR, medical writing and CRO companies competing on the basis of cost for pharma business are not bound by the protocols that bind pharmaceutical companies.

The bottom line is that where there had been full access to clinical trial data before 1980, there was less access after that and by 2000 no access. Where ghostwriting of medical articles had been rare, it became universal for on-patent drugs. The greatest concentration of Fake News on the planet lies in the medical literature produced to sell on-patent drugs.

For industry, clinical trials are tools to secure a marketing advantage or counter adverse publicity. They are not designed to establish what drugs do or who might or might not be helped by them.

Control of clinical trial data as well as control of what appears to be science but is in fact a marketing script means this industry has realized the goal of propaganda, which is to become invisible, more successfully than anyone else has ever been able to do.

Why No Revolution?

In 1807, Johann Gottlieb Fichte in the wake of a Prussian defeat by France challenged the education system to introduce Evidence-Based Thinking, dialectics, to counter a sterile philosophy that put more emphasis on rhetoric—now called propaganda or marketing. Prussia overhauled its educational system, but philosophy ended up replaced by a science built on taking propositions (theses) into the real world and generating contrary instances (antitheses) leading to a dynamic synthesis.

Forty years later, Marx called for Evidence-Based Living—a dialectical materialism. The working class and bourgeoisie would take their ideas of what was right and proper in terms of work into factories and cities, and encountering adverse outcomes, and a new awareness of what the commodification of outputs meant, in reaching for a new synthesis would inevitably advance humanity. The revolution never happened. The working class became a middle class, and a rising tide of affluence later washed away group cohesion in the face of alienating conditions.

In 1990, Evidence-Based Medicine proposed a dialectical operationalism, with doctors as the revolutionary class. Clinicians would take the theses derived from clinical trials into clinical situations, where the encounter with contrary instances and patient values would lead to a new synthesis. The revolution never happened. Instead a medical proletariat are now more bound into the apparatus of industrial health systems than they were in 1990.

September 20, 1991 is a key date in this history. In February 1990, an article in the *American Journal of Psychiatry* had outlined the cases of six people who had become suicidal on Eli Lilly's recently released SSRI antidepressant Prozac (fluoxetine), then on its way to blockbuster status despite minimal RCT evidence for benefits. The suicidality had appeared on treatment, stopped when treatment stopped and reappeared on restarting. By all canons of causality, Prozac had caused suicidality. FDA were forced into a hearing on Prozac. In preparation, Lilly compiled its RCT data, which was submitted as an article to *BMJ*.

The editor of *BMJ*, Richard Smith, was an early fan of EBM, which he saw as a way to control the pharmaceutical industry. Faced with this article, Smith saw Lilly seemingly embracing EBM, despite the small print showing an increased risk of suicide on Prozac compared to placebo. Nevertheless, the *BMJ* conveniently ran Lilly's article on Prozac on September 20, the day of the FDA hearings. The article became a key exhibit in Lilly's media defence: the plural of anecdote is not data. Who are you going to believe, the anecdotes or the data? Lilly's defence also hinged on a mantra: "It's the disease not the drug".

The original phrase "the plural of anecdote is data" was coined by Raymond Wolfinger, a polling expert in 1969. Google wouldn't work if this weren't true. But the CEO of Nutrasweet claimed "the plural of anecdotes is not data" in 1971 when his company's sweetener, aspartame, became embroiled in a cancer scare. The related phrases "anecdotes are not science" and "harm has not been proven" were also coined at this time and used in media interviews by spokesmen for the Pedophile Information Exchange in the 1970s to defend sexual relations between adults and children. They are now the stock in trade of corporate risk management.

FDA was sitting on RCT evidence showing that older antidepressants were more effective than the SSRIs and showing that the soon-to-be-released Zoloft (sertraline) and Paxil (paroxetine) also increased the risk of suicide. FDA concealed these data and cleared Prozac, saying the fuss was a public relations issue and that warnings would deter people from seeking treatment. Up to 15% of the population in many countries now take SSRIs chronically, a large proportion of whom do so because they are physically addicted.

Medicine changed on September 20. After this date, journals faced a choice between articles reporting RCTs or meta-analyses of RCTs with companies paying a fortune for reprints, or case reports, up till then the mainstream of medical publishing. Journal lawyers advised against publication of case reports on treatment hazards now that the traditional methods of establishing cause and effect no longer seemed to apply. Up till 2000, most doctors had a steady stream of drugs' bulletins assessing new drugs and detailing their hazards, but these became unprofitable and largely vanished, replaced by Guidelines, which list drug benefits but not hazards. As a result, it can now take 20 years or more for a significant hazard to be accepted.

Twenty years later in 2011, under a new editor *BMJ* ran a celebrated campaign centered on the efforts of Peter Doshi and Tom Jefferson to access the data on the antiviral drug Tamiflu. On the back of articles claiming it was effective, governments stockpiled billions of dollars' worth of Tamiflu to handle pandemic flu. But every time Doshi and Jefferson accessed the results of another study Tamiflu's apparent efficacy slipped until it was non-existent. Sales of Tamiflu, however, held up. Why? Because there were still no adverse event data and just as water will flow down the most minimal of gradients in the absence of bumps, so in the absence of harms even hints of efficacy sell drugs.

The various NGOs and purchasing bodies seeking access to high-cost drugs to date have not understood this point. When negotiating a price based on efficacy, even if the efficacy is minimal, refusing to buy puts them in a position of rationing treatments. Accessing adverse-event data would transform their position. Rather than an access to medicines movement, we now need an Access to Real Medicines (ARMs) movement, where real means the harms data.

Simply stating an RCT has not been done now ends most discussions, notwithstanding the fact that once a serious problem has been identified it would be unethical to run an RCT. For instance, despite convincing epidemiological and biological evidence SSRIs increase miscarriage rates, cause cardiac and other birth defects, and lead to autistic spectrum disorder (ASD) and neurodevelopmental delay, and billions of dollars in verdicts against them for these injuries, all companies need to do to get doctors onside is to say no RCTs have been done.

Faced with reports of ASD on SSRIs, companies set up internal teratology, pharmacology, epidemiology, pharmacovigilance, and psychology groups, each tasked to review the evidence from their area of expertise. While the overall picture may be compelling, the chances of any one box containing cast iron evidence is less. For "the sake of objectivity", the work will be coordinated by someone with no background in these issues. If asked whether the work-groups took into account studies showing developmental delay on SSRIs, they will likely respond: "I have no expertise to decide whether we should do that or not, my brief was to get the groups to review any published articles that had the term ASD in them".

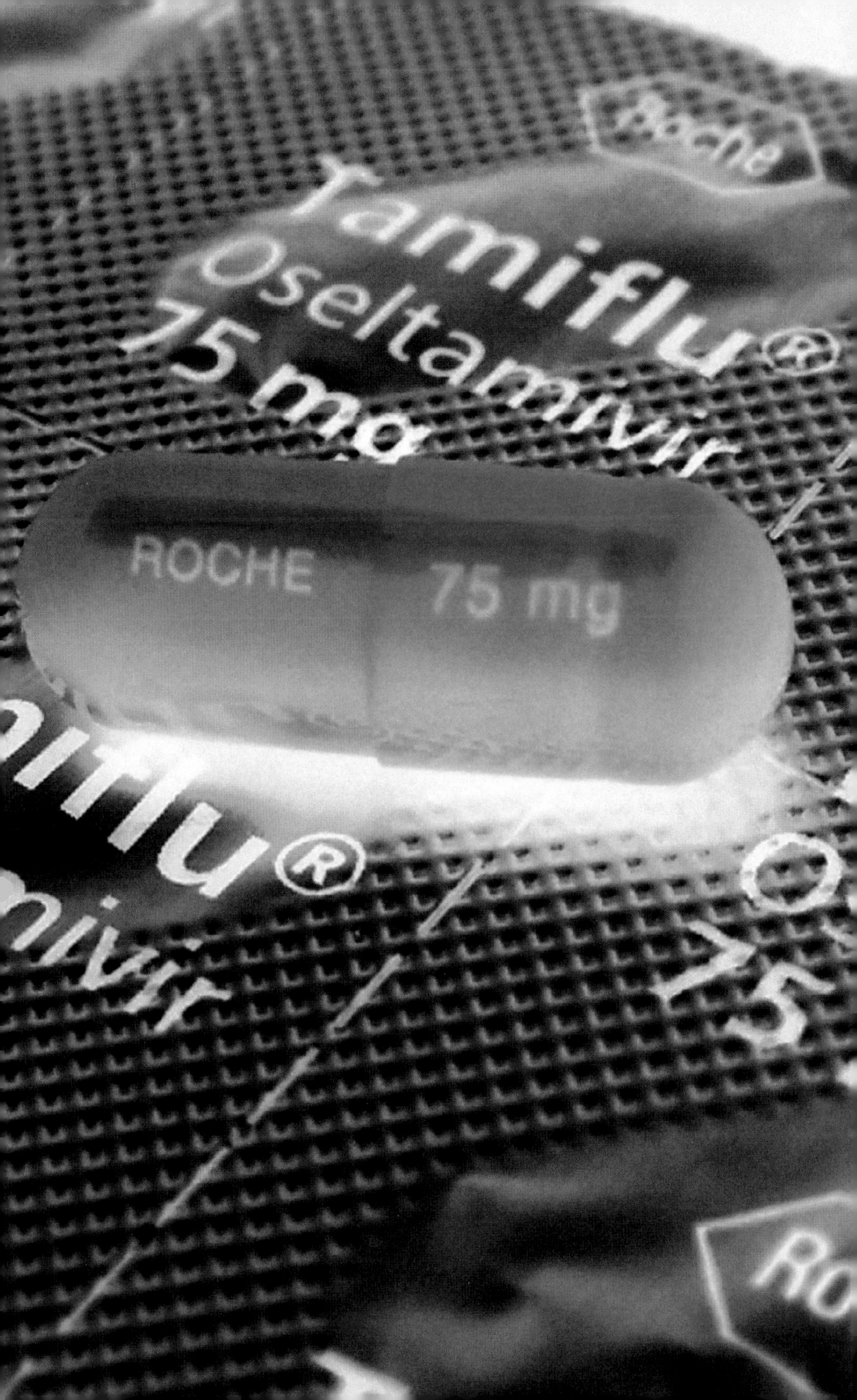
Roche
Tamiflu®
Oseltamivir
75 mg
ROCHE
75 mg

There is nothing psychopathic about this, any more than there was about German technicians discussing the specifications needed for transport vehicles to cater for defecation and urination en route to Auschwitz; it's a technical issue.

Since September 1991, we and our doctors are up against the science. When someone becomes suicidal on an antidepressant or some other problem happens on a drug, the scientific task is to establish whether the drug has caused the problem. This is done by taking a history, doing an examination and perhaps laboratory tests, looking for competing explanations and where possible stopping and then reintroducing the drug, altering the dose or adding an antidote. Once the best possible judgment is made, if there is an apparent mismatch between that and the purported science, it is not scientific to discard the clinical judgment. It should throw up a new scientific task—explaining the mismatch. In the case of SSRIs and suicidality, and most drug wrecks, the mismatch stems from a lack of access to the data and a ghostwriting of the clinical literature.

Instead facing women with deep vein thrombosis (DVT) on oral contraceptives doctors now are more likely to check the evidence base and finding nothing placebo-controlled there defer to a bureaucrat who is in FDA because they don't like engaging with people, who may have briefly practiced orthopedics when the drug is a contraceptive, and who on consulting company reports from the subset of company RCTs sent to FDA has no incentive to spot a problem hidden under a coding rubric in the way he might if the data were in the public domain. In stepping back from making a diagnosis, or coming to a verdict, doctors have betrayed their birthright.

We as a result have become invisible to doctors and health systems. Should something go wrong on treatment for us or someone we care about, and we seek to find out what has happened, we will be met by a sympathetic health team armed with a root-cause analysis who will point to the fact that all guidelines were adhered to, and all benchmarks for quality of service met. We will be left baffled.

It cannot be otherwise unless the analytic pathway includes a box for treatment-induced death. But a box for medicine-induced death or injury can't be there without pathways to mitigate that risk. And these cannot be put in place without confronting the fact that there is no access to the data and most of the literature is ghostwritten. It is above the paygrade of a health service CEO or even a Minister of Health to put such a box in place. But there is no need for them to fret, as anyone suggesting that large sections of the *New England Journal of Medicine* are junk would get dismissed out of hand.

Children

In 2001, an article appeared in the journal with the highest impact factor in child psychiatry, and a distinguished authorship line, claiming paroxetine worked well and was safe for depressed children. The internal GlaxoSmithKline designation for this study was Study 329.

As of 2001, there had been approximately 70 publications of so-called "open-label" studies (i.e., trials conducted without a control group) giving antidepressants to children, which claimed they worked wonderfully well. RCTs are done to temper the enthusiasm of reports like these. If a treatment doesn't work in an RCT, clinicians stop using it.

Study 329 came into a clearer focus in 2003 and 2004 because of media interest in the growing use of psychotropic drugs for children. Grounds emerged to suspect that Study 329 was not all it appeared to be and that paroxetine was making children suicidal. These revelations led to a regulatory crisis. Further investigation revealed that up to

2004, there had actually been 20 RCTs on the use of antidepressants with children and that all of them had been ghost-written or company-written and all had produced negative results. The trials also showed a consistent excess of suicidal events with paroxetine treatment.

In 2001 the FDA and other regulators had approved fluoxetine (Prozac) for depressed children based on two trials which were published with positive results, but which had actually produced negative results. In 2002, the FDA similarly issued an approvable letter for paroxetine also based on negative trials, before growing media interest prevented paroxetine from being marketed.

Since then, there have been a further 10 trials of antidepressants in children, making 30 in total with over 10,000 children recruited. All of the trials produced negative results. This is the greatest concentration of negative trials for any indication ever recorded. Yet the sales of antidepressants in children are increasing rapidly and these drugs, barring the oral contraceptives, now appear to be the most commonly used drugs by teenage girls.

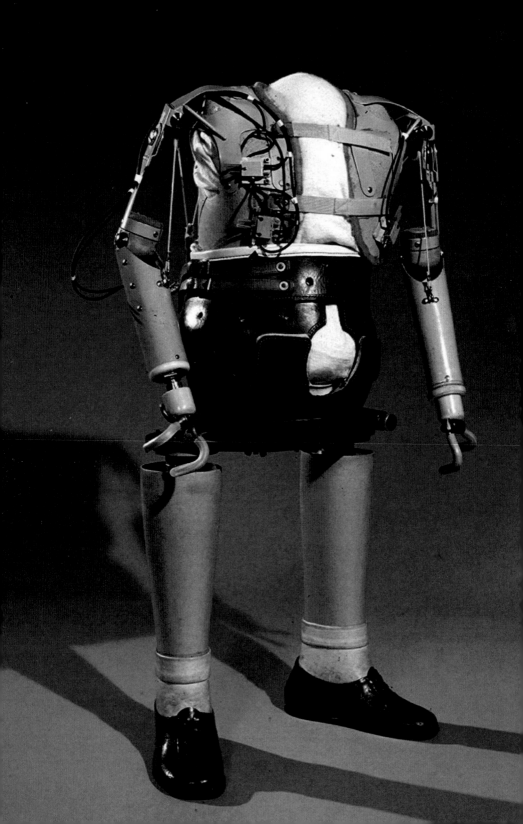

Crisis of Technique

Medicines combine a chemical technology and information. Where once the information came from the lived experience of doctors and patients, since 1980 it primarily stems from techniques that companies manage.

Techniques effect predictable changes. They are one-dimensional and can seem value-free but aren't. Because they are effective, techniques generalise, globalise and push toward technocracy, delivering power and capital to those who hold them. They are seductive enough to have Israeli and convicted Nazi scientists working together on projects like thalidomide in the 1960s.

The apparent value-neutrality of techniques appeals to scientists. Science is impossible without technologies. But science itself is not value-neutral. It is committed to asking questions no matter how awkward, and to complete transparency as regards to data. Neither of these conditions is met by the modern pharmaceutical industry.

A globalisation of effective technologies would face us with ultimate questions. The limit form of this lies in Full A.I.—Full Technique —which risks handing over responsibility and control irretrievably to an "alien", or to whoever controls the alien, leaving everyone else dependent on the goodwill of this "being".

Whether we get faced with Full Technique, we are faced with and will be faced with effective technologies mixed with even more effective behavioural techniques, capable of persuading us that less effective technologies are an advance on what we had before. In this sense, drugs and the wrecks they bring are a window on bigger issues rather than the only concern.

For two centuries it appeared that the technologies underpinning physics, chemistry and biology occupied a different domain to the human sciences which, while there have been steady advances in neuroscience, had replication envy—they didn't work reliably. Although largely overlooked, this potency problem was solved with the development of Pavlovian conditioning, building on foundations laid by John Locke and further developed by Skinner, along with data from applied psychology. These data increasingly shape social media platforms, and underpin behavioural economics, a now flourishing domain, garnering Nobel Prizes. We are rapidly moving to a point of being able to control Man as much as Nature.

Rather than working for us as technologies from automobiles, to X-rays and guns have done, the mix of behavioural techniques with other technologies within health has destroyed healthcare and is generating a hostile environment. Health Apps and other social media seem likely to diminish us further rather than enhance us.

All techniques involve a fix, an automatic mechanism, which produces effects. Problems can arise simply from the ease of adoption of a technique, and our turn to techniques today is caught in quips about ours being a quick fix culture. There can be hazards from the technique itself. In addition, the benefits we have derived from techniques bias us toward thinking that a new technology will on balance will be better than an older one. This bias is increasingly aggravated by the behavioural techniques that conceal the mismatch between new technologies and our expectations.

Guns are an exemplary technology. They solve significant problems. Once in place, their use triggers an arms race as whoever holds the most effective techniques holds power. Guns can save lives but proposals to have good guys with guns in schools to control school shootings raise the prospect of multiplying up the availability and use of guns, and letting them leak into situations, where our sense is they may to do more harm than good, both in terms of lives lost but also in terms of a loss of our ability to conceive of and secure alternate and in the longer run better solutions.

The development of the nuclear bomb revealed an unexpected limit to one-dimensional technologies. With the bomb we reached a point where the efficacy at our disposal could no longer be employed. Vietnam won on the battlefield whatever about winning the "peace".

Orthodox medical techniques have for the most part over the last two centuries enhanced rather than diminished us. Life expectancies have risen because of these techniques, in a way that would not have happened had homeopathy, complementary, ayurvedic or other approaches dominated health.

But as with the bomb, we now appear to have reached a limit to an unthinking application of medical technique. Having been the best in the world in the 1960s, American life expectancy, which had been falling relative to other countries for four decades, has now fallen in absolute terms for five years in a row, for the first time since the American Civil War.

In the 1980s, few people were on more than short courses of one drug per day. As of 2018, 40% of over 45s are on three or more drugs every day of the year and 40% of over 65s on five or more drugs. As of 2010, there has been evidence that reducing medication burden to five or less increases life expectancy, reduces hospitalization rate and enhances the quality of life.

Even when deaths are put down to cancer and cardiovascular causes rather than the drugs used to treat them, treatments emerge as the third greatest cause of death in hospitals and almost have to be therefore the leading cause of death in community settings where the illnesses are less severe. Given that pretty well everyone on even one drug is disabled to some extent, treatments must also be the greatest source of disability on the planet.

Aside from falling life expectancy, the rising costs of health services risk toppling economies, while at the same time there is a degradation of the quality of care. As far as care goes, the health services economy could now be described as Upper Volta with Missiles as the USSR was just before it imploded. This is not a simple inequality issue. While those who are least well-off are more prone to ill-health than the rich, a greater intensity of health services harms and kills whatever social class you come from. We need to find a way to stop living the lives pharma wants us to live.

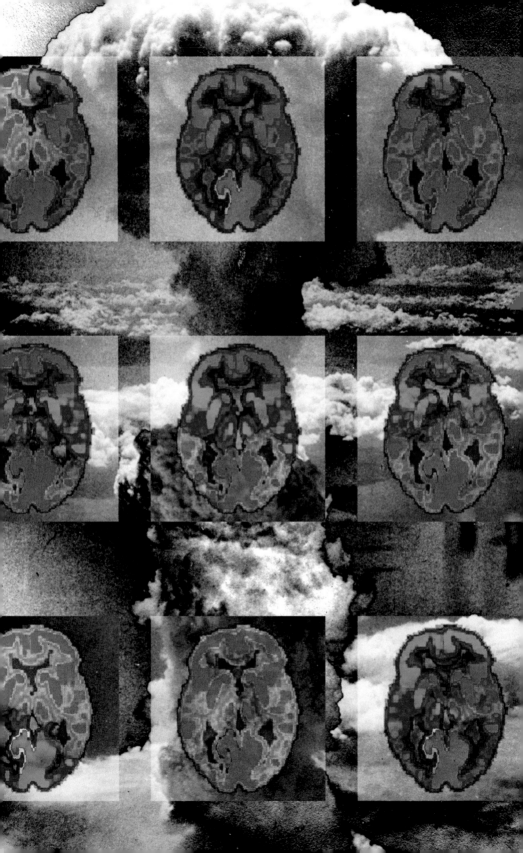

A Call to H.ARMs

At the heart of this call are four ideas.

- Organising health in terms of care is more economic than providing health services.

- Health-Care embraces drugs that are poisons; health services can't.

- Drug wrecks cut to the heart of modern politics. Suffer an injury from treatment, or approach this issue in any way, and you too can have a Tiananmen Square moment.

- Grappling with drug wrecks needs an act of judgment, a diagnosis—a vote. The politics of drug wrecks tie into questions of power and democracy.

The need to diagnose is forced on us by the consequences of over-prescribing. We have reached a point where we need to take stock of what we want and choose between options. This needs collaboration. We need a *Discernimus Ergo Sumus* ("We make judgment together and therefore we are.") rather than Luther's credo *Ergo Sum* ("I believe and therefore I am") or Descartes' *Cogito Ergo Sum* ("I think and therefore I am").

Drug wrecks will always stand as a challenge to our technologies. When put into human bodies, chemicals always have at least a hundred effects. Many of the 99 other effects may be more important to us than the one effect of interest to a pharmaceutical or health service company. This is also where our perfectly sensible bias to fix problems with a fix runs up against the difficulty of making a pill for polypharmacy.

Drug wrecks force us to confront the increasingly potent behavioural techniques—from branding to rhetoric/propaganda to RCTs—that when we are injured encourage the herd to move on, leaving us behind. Drug wrecks call for solidarity—but how to achieve it?

At the heart of these issues lies a question of objectivity. The value-neutral operational thinking that currently dominates medicine portrays objectivity as something that has a virgin birth from a mechanical apparatus. Whether the RCT organ-grinders work for a drug company or a group critical of drug companies, the result of an RCT will always be the same.

Drug wrecks make clear that objectivity arises when Christians, Muslims, Jews and Atheists are faced with data genuinely generated, given the opportunity to repeat the test or undertake other tests to explore the data, and challenged to agree how the data might be explained. It doesn't come from a mechanical apparatus.

When we bring a report of some change following intake of a drug to a doctor, we will almost always be right—the world wouldn't work if we weren't. If we test our perception with a medical person with experience in this area and possibly a bias toward seeing the benefits of drugs and not their hazards, and they agree the drug has likely caused the problem, this bolsters our claim for objectivity.

As things stand, however, unlike pilots who report adverse events and won't fly if the problem is not cleared up, most doctors will not agree with us in public even if they agree in private. Many get nasty at what appears to them as a challenge to their authority. And they are supported in this by both the supposed evidence-base and will be by social media which seems to be gearing up to mark any discussion of adverse events as Fake News.

If we can find doctors or others willing to stand with us and can build maps of where they are, it might be possible to restore healthcare and make it sustainable.

Anonymity

Key to our current difficulties is a successful branding of considered clinical judgements as anecdotes.

When drug wrecked, we must also grapple with the fact that the few clinical judgements doctors send to regulators have their identifying details stripped from them. This transforms them into hearsay and makes them impossible to assess for cause and effect and inadmissible in court.

Meanwhile, companies have framed clinical trial informed-consent forms to include a statement that our details will never be revealed to anyone. Our signatures enable companies to withhold our data. Baited with confidentiality, our participation in trials drops us and everyone we know into a state of legal jeopardy. This company move should transform their trials into hearsay—if we had the motivation to make it so.

Access to our data is a no-brainer. Company power hinges on a denial of access. Given they have gone out of their way for several decades to avoid making drugs that save lives, they need us more than we need them—and Triple Therapy and Gleevec aside—it will cost us almost nothing to refuse to take any drugs produced since 1990 without access to the data.

We need Access to Real Medicines (ARMs)—hence this Call to H.ARMs.

Guides

For two centuries good doctors have been our guides through the hell of disease and the purgatory of treatment. The notion of a liberal professional was born with the medical model. This was an individual who exercised a degree of discretion in healthcare encounters. We viewed this input, on balance, as beneficial where previously we viewed doctors with scorn. The new discretion was best embodied by Philippe Pinel when stating that wonderful though it is to have remedies, it is an even greater art to know when not to use them.

For a century, the provision of certain medicines on prescription-only, a police technique, has defined medical professionalism. Where once doctors were in principle aware that drugs were poisons from which good might be brought, and surgeries were mutilations, with the magic of the medical encounter lying in the doctor, in the 1980s this kind of care was rebranded as a cottage industry. Medicines were transformed from poisons to sacraments that reliably lowered blood pressure, blood sugars and blood cholesterol or thickened bones and diagnosis was reconfigured in a manner that made discretion a problem rather than a virtue.

Doctors are no more virtuous than anyone else. Put them in the wrong system and they will oppose Sara Josephine Baker's preventive medicine as bad for medical business, as they did in 1916. They will be complicit with an elimination of those perceived as "unfit" as they were in the 1940s. In the 1980s, it took minimal financial inducements to turn doctors into agents of public or private corporations who had little difficulty putting patients on 10 or more drugs they would never take themselves.

Even as they claim to be scientists, doctors have now slid into a position of compliance with a sequestration of clinical trial data, and ghostwriting of the medical literature that turns ineffective and dangerous drugs into miraculous blockbusters, even when those injured or killed are minors. Even as they claim to be professionals, they adhere to guidelines—a role for technicians rather than professionals.

Still, faced with diseases, if it's healthcare we want, whether we provide it as a collective, or by individual contract, we need help to handle the internal contradiction involved in bringing good from the use of a poison or mutilation. Help that might require non-doing. We need to reclaim a path that lies between the proficiency of a technician and an ivory tower expertise. We need a guide who works with us rather than for a corporation.

Drugs and devices are like erotic attraction—too promiscuous to confine within the confines of a contractual relationship. Still we need to separate a domain in which our natural instincts as consumers, ideally supported by consumer associations, can come into play to manage our dis-ease as we see fit, from another one in which drugs and devices are used for diseases.

This may no longer be possible. Doctors are now largely rule-takers (vassals) in systems where pharmacy-benefit companies, the makers of electronic health records, insurance companies and others dictate which drugs any of us get for either disease or dis-ease. For the moment, these systems find it useful to maintain a medical simulacrum and may continue to do so while the expense is not too great. If doctors are to have a substantive role in this new world, they will need to make some difficult and important choices.

There may be little option but to wait in the hope that just as rising sea-levels either trigger a sense of common purpose, or a new extermination agenda, perhaps at seconds to midnight, as happened with the weapons race, falling life expectancies will lead to a new openness to take our values into account to make healthcare great again.

Techniques are from Mars, Magic from Venus

Technique is at the heart of this analysis, but this is not an argument against techniques. Deep brain stimulation, gene editing and other techniques can be put to good use—if we can trust our doctors and ourselves.

But all techniques that work attract capital and power and this potentially puts them at odds with us. Nowhere is this clearer than in health. The spread of techniques has created health services that bring us health problems we never knew we had, and the consumption of these services may now be reducing our life expectancies. The measuring instruments and a turn to operationalism that a technical culture fosters seek, in the name of standardization, to remove our and our doctor's judgment from the frame.

Healthcare, in contrast, happens when we bring a problem to a doctor who makes a judgment call on our behalf and in collaboration with us as part of an act of Care. This kind of Care involves magic— bringing good out of the use of a poison or mutilation. Magic like this does not compute for insurers or technocrats.

If we agree to be poisoned or mutilated, reasonably confident our doctor would do the same for herself or a member of her family, even if things go wrong, trust is built. A social capital accumulates. But if we are persuaded to take a drug for osteoporosis or nerves or to lower our lipids—many doctors would not consume the services we are offered— and something goes wrong and we figure s/he would not have taken the treatment herself, this betrayal destroys trust and wipes out that social capital.

The most visible demonstration of a gritty Care is if a drug treatment goes wrong or a service malfunctions, and our doctor supports us against the organization she works for or the pharmaceutical industry.

In 1848, Liberals like Virchow and Communists like Marx saw the aristocracy, which had governed the agricultural sector, withering away replaced by a new manufacturing sector—which brought us the spectre of an Iron Cage of bureaucracy. Manufacturing has now been replaced by a service sector whose managers have shut the lock on that cage.

Robots will likely deliver our food in restaurants soon, answer our insurance or banking queries and deliver health services, providing even "care" functions in retirement homes and hospitals. Even religion may come in commodified forms, a McMindfulness.

How we handle this is a moral question. Techniques are amoral. They make a virtue of indifference. All use of technique involves some stepping back from care and responsibility. It's up to us to Care —to see to it that we are enhanced rather than diminished when we turn to a technique. Good intentions are not enough. We must take responsibility for the outcomes. Care in this sense needs judgment calls made in relationships.

In 1848, a world where our family, tribe, or clan were central to our identity was giving way to larger groupings of class and nation. With today's challenges, if humanity is not the group that attracts our allegiance, some of us face extermination and the humanity of all will be diminished.

Illustrations

All illustrations by Billiam James except as noted above.

About David Healy

David Healy is a psychiatrist, psychopharmacologist, scientist and author. He is now based at the Department of Family Medicine, in Canada's McMaster University. He is a co-founder of RxISK.org, an adverse event reporting website, and the co-founder of Samizdat Health Writer's Co-operative Inc. Healy's research covers treatment-induced problems, and the history of physical treatments in medicine. He has written more than 200 peer-reviewed articles, 200 other articles, and 24 books, including *The Antidepressant Era, Let Them Eat Prozac,* and *Pharmageddon.*

Praise for *The Decapitation of Care*

"*David Healy is widely known and respected for his trenchant critiques of the problems associated with psychopharmacology. Here, he broadens his critique to suggest that the failings of the modern medical system are a major explanation for one of the most important and neglected stories of our time, recent sharp declines in life expectancy in advanced industrial societies, including Britain and the United States.*"

Andrew Scull, author of Madness in Civilization

"*Thought-provoking and important... In Decapitation of Care, David Healy takes readers through a quick review of the history of "healthcare," and details how, in the modern age, commerce and a profession's adoption of so-called "evidence-based medicine" has led to medical care that over-medicates, over-diagnoses, and does great harm to our health.*"

Robert Whitaker, author of Anatomy of an Epidemic

Manufactured by Amazon.ca
Bolton, ON

11246020R10045